1977

Automobiles will help you arrive,
But only
If you know
How to drive.

Ride with Me
Through
ABC

Scroll Press, Inc., New York

Pictures by Horst Lemke

Story by Susan Bond

© Sigbert Mohn Verlag 1965
First U.S. publication by Scroll Press, Inc. 1968
Second U.S. printing by Scroll Press, Inc. 1970
All rights reserved.
Library of Congress Catalog Card Number 67-19376
Printed in West Germany

If you've somewhere to go,
Some place you must be,
Let's travel there via ABC.

Boats go by water, I'm sure you know,
And especially well with Daddy to row.

Chinese junks for a spree when the place you must be
Is bobbing along on the wide wavy sea.

Dauntless Captain, steer your ship,
And take us on an ocean trip.

Engineers can guide their trains
  Through glowing sun and flowing rains.

Flying a plane is a swift way to go,
  But of course you must have a pilot, you know.

Gondolas are fun if it's Venice you seek,
And equally right for the top of a peak.

Helicopters are worth a try.
Doesn't it look like a dragon fly?

Icarus, the ancient one,
   Made wings of wax to fly to the sun.
   The sun was hot, the wings got sticky.
   And so — goodbye to poor old Icky.

Jolly boats can sail the seas,
But they don't go far
without a breeze.

Klippety, klop. It's such a lark
Riding coaches through the park.

Loads large and small
Truck drivers haul
Through winter and summer,
Through spring and fall.

Motorcycles
roar and whiz.
They are **not**
for little kids!

Noah's great Ark could have taken you, too.
What fun to ride in a seafaring zoo!

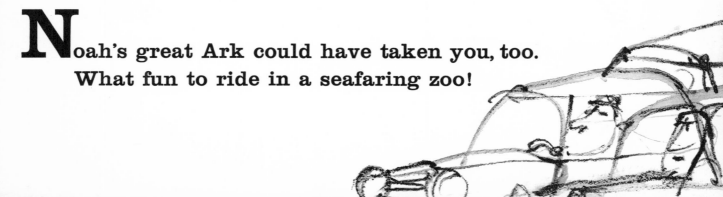

Omnibus drivers roar through traffic,
Swerving, curving — quite fantastic!

Prancing hunting horses could
Carry you through the deepest wood.

Quickly cross the desert sand
In a camel caravan.

Riding scooters is lots of fun.
Too bad there's room for only one.

Squeeze into a streetcar, Sweet,
  And ride on someone else's feet.

Tractors plod across the way
Leaving horses to their hay.

Underwater the mermaid is seen
Catching a ride on a submarine.

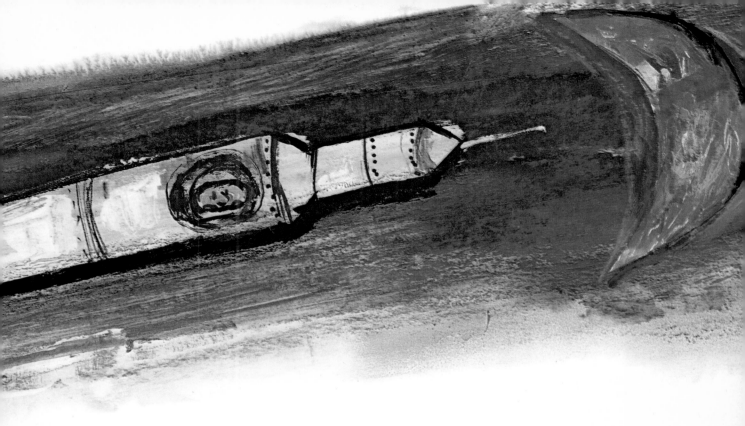

View the Alps from a cycler's bike.
Up, up, up, that's quite a hike!

Wondrous spaceship through heavens hurled.
I hear the ride is out of this world.

X-stasy it would be
  To soar through clouds of fantasy.

Yachts go knots
  Through lots of spots.

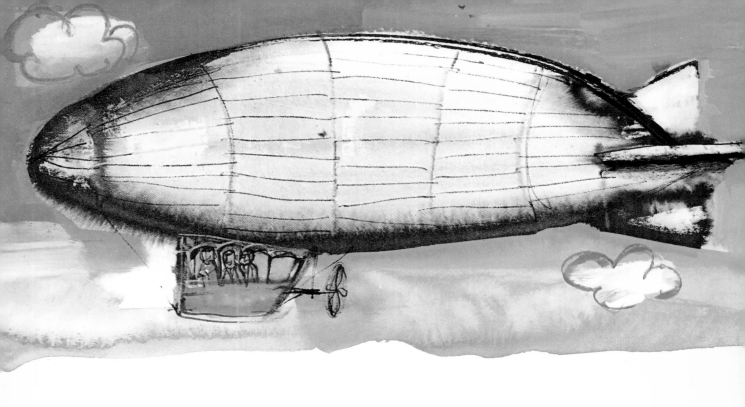

Zeppelins soar o'er the steeple.
All that blimp for so few people?

Take whichever way you please
Traveling through the ABCs.